Usborne
Build your ow
ROBOTS
Sticker Book

Illustrated by Reza Ilyasa

Designed by Marc Maynard
Written by Simon Tudhope

Contents

In 3306AD the robots on Planet Tempest turned against their creators.
Humans had built them to fight their wars, but the machines rebelled and drove them from
the planet. With the humans gone the robots could have lived in peace, but these machines
were built for war. Two armies formed and the battle for Planet Tempest began...

Goliath

Smashing through buildings and swatting missiles aside, Goliath slices ten robots in half with one swipe of his blade.

STATISTICS

- **HEIGHT:** 50m (164ft)
- **WEAPON:** bladehammer
- **ARMY:** Volton
- **STRENGTH:** incredible strength and toughness
- **WEAKNESS:** slow, no long-range weapon

Leviathan

Leviathan emerges from the sea to wreak havoc on land. He nails his prey with a giant harpoon then drags it down into the depths.

STATISTICS

- **HEIGHT:** 40m (131ft)
- **WEAPONS:** harpoon, missiles
- **ARMY:** Scorax
- **STRENGTH:** speed, power
- **WEAKNESS:** harpoon slow to reload if it misses its target

Spike

Tearing across the desert, sending thick dust clouds into the air, Spike closes on his target with terrifying speed.

STATISTICS

- **HEIGHT:** 15m (49ft)
- **WEAPONS:** machine gun, chainsword
- **ARMY:** Volton
- **STRENGTH:** very fast and agile
- **WEAKNESS:** easily damaged

Pincer

Pincer uses stun guns to disable other robots and send them crashing to the ground. Then it scuttles in close to tear them apart.

STATISTICS

- **HEIGHT:** 10m (33ft)
- **WEAPONS:** stun guns, tail claw
- **ARMY:** Scorax
- **STRENGTH:** toughness, watchfulness and wariness
- **WEAKNESS:** no heavy weaponry, small size

Outlaw

Outlaw's arrows rip through the air like bolts
of lightning. Perched high above the ruined city,
he can strike his target from over a mile away.

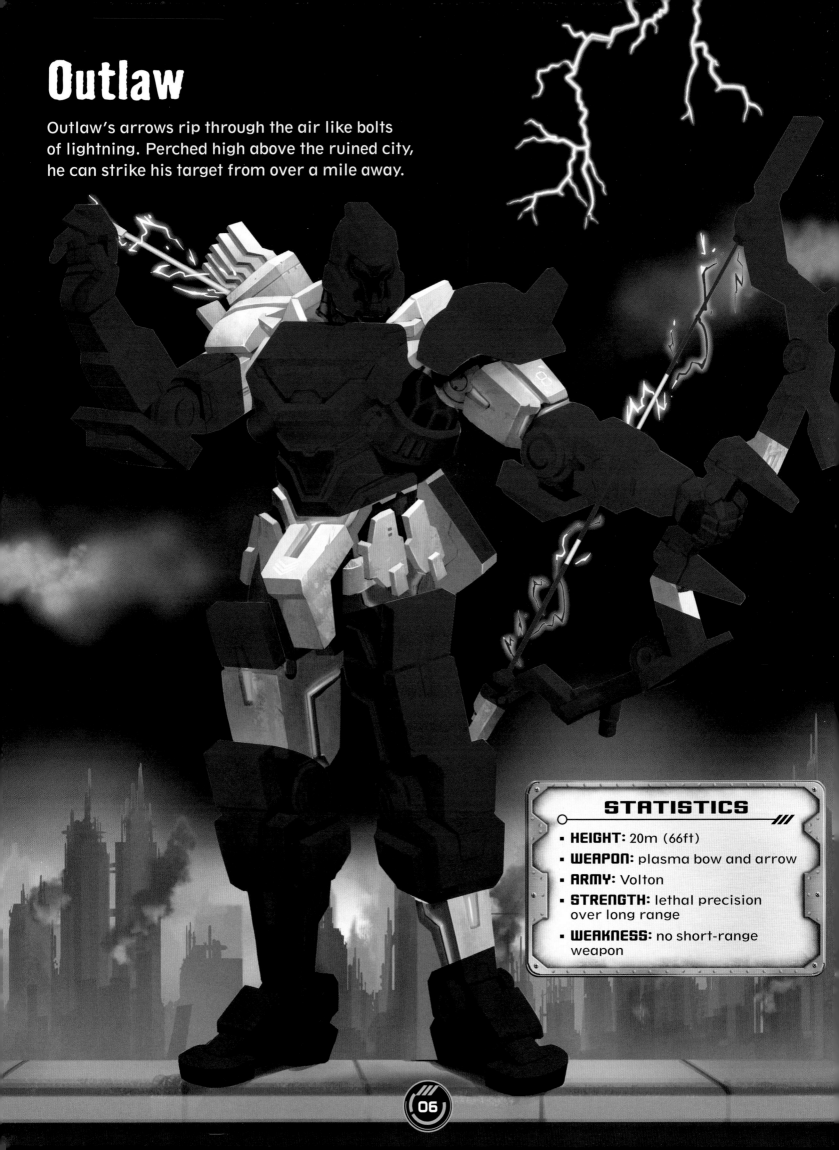

STATISTICS

- **HEIGHT:** 20m (66ft)
- **WEAPON:** plasma bow and arrow
- **ARMY:** Volton
- **STRENGTH:** lethal precision over long range
- **WEAKNESS:** no short-range weapon

Glitch

Glitch turns robots into giant metal puppets.
Hacking into their systems and seizing control,
it creates an army of traitors that attack
their own side.

Kremator

Kremator has lava flowing through his core. Shooting jets of flame from either hand, he turns his enemies into liquid metal.

Bolt

Clearing entire buildings in one leap, Bolt strikes his target from high in the sky, then lands with a crunch to finish the job.

STATISTICS

- **HEIGHT:** 20m (66ft)
- **WEAPON:** laser cannon
- **ARMY:** Volton
- **STRENGTH:** agility, speed
- **WEAKNESS:** vulnerable to heavy fire without his shield

Ironstein

Strapped inside this giant machine is a tiny red robot with a brilliant mind. He's called Ironstein, and he's risen through the ranks to lead the Scorax army.

Wrench

Wrench doesn't fight in the war and doesn't have a side. He just patiently waits for the battle to end then trundles out to treat the wounded.

STATISTICS

- **HEIGHT:** 15m (49ft)
- **WEAPON:** n/a
- **ARMY:** n/a
- **STRENGTH:** useful to both sides
- **WEAKNESS:** not designed for battle

Katana

Katana closes on his enemy, slicing bullets in half before they can touch him. Then with a triumphant roar he strikes the deadly blow.

Kreeper

Kreeper lurks in dark tunnels until it hears footsteps overhead. Then with a terrifying screech it bursts from the ground and sinks its jaws into its victim.

STATISTICS

- **LENGTH:** 60m (197ft)
- **WEAPONS:** jaw daggers, laser cannon
- **ARMY:** Scorax
- **STRENGTH:** stealth, size
- **WEAKNESS:** vulnerable if detected

Magnotron

In the belly of this beast is a magnetic core so powerful it can suck up every robot on the battlefield. They disappear with a despairing cry and are never seen again.

Titan

This fearless warrior is leader of the Voltons. His great sword flashes as he holds it up high and his mighty roar echoes: "VOLTONS ATTACK... ATTACK... ATTACK!"

Chrysis

Chrysis swoops on enemies like a demon from the skies. Swerving past missiles and rockets he leaves his target with nowhere to run.

STATISTICS

- **HEIGHT:** 20m (66ft)
- **WEAPONS:** missiles, grenade launcher
- **ARMY:** Scorax
- **STRENGTH:** speed, agility
- **WEAKNESS:** fragile wings

Enforcer

Enforcer is the most heavily-armed robot on the planet. Under fierce enemy fire he stomps across the battlefield to terminate his target.

Reza

Reza's blades slice through the air as he leaps from the shadows. His target spins around as the first one bites... but it's already too late.

STATISTICS

- **HEIGHT:** 15m (49ft)
- **WEAPON:** ninja blades
- **ARMY:** Scorax
- **STRENGTH:** stealth, agility, speed
- **WEAKNESS:** easily damaged

Buzzsaw

Buzzsaw revs his blades and hurls himself into battle. With an ear-splitting screech and a blaze of sparks he tears his opponent into scrap metal.

STATISTICS

- **HEIGHT:** 25m (82ft)
- **WEAPONS:** buzzsaw, chainsaw
- **ARMY:** Scorax
- **STRENGTH:** ferocious in close-quarters combat
- **WEAKNESS:** no long-range weapon

Nemesis

This relentless hunter tracks down robots that have deserted their army. Wherever they run and wherever they hide, there's no escape from Nemesis.

Vertigo

Vertigo's anti-gravity gun crackles with energy. He blasts an enemy robot high into the sky... and watches it crash to earth with a sickening crunch.

Blizzard

Roaming the frozen wastelands of the
north, Blizzard freezes his enemies
solid, then – SMASH! – he shatters
them with his hammer.

STATISTICS ///

- **HEIGHT:** 25m (82ft)
- **WEAPONS:** freeze ray,
  warhammer
- **ARMY:** Volton
- **STRENGTH:** strength, toughness
- **WEAKNESS:** no long-range weapon

Glossary

- **ANTI-GRAVITY GUN:** fires an anti-gravity beam that lifts heavy objects into the air as if they were weightless

- **HARPOON:** a weapon that looks like a large spear with a rope attached. The spear sticks into its target and the rope reels it in.

- **PLANET TEMPEST:** a planet that was colonized by humans in 3209 AD, because it was rich in metals and oil.

- **SCORAX:** an army of robots led by Ironstein

- **STUN GUN:** a weapon that knocks out a robot's electronic systems with a powerful pulse of energy

- **STUN NET:** an electrified net that knocks out a robot's electronic systems

- **VOLTON:** an army of robots led by Titan

Digital manipulation by Keith Furnival
Edited by Sam Taplin

First published in 2014 by Usborne Publishing Ltd, Usborne House, 83-85 Saffron Hill, London EC1N 8RT, England. www.usborne.com

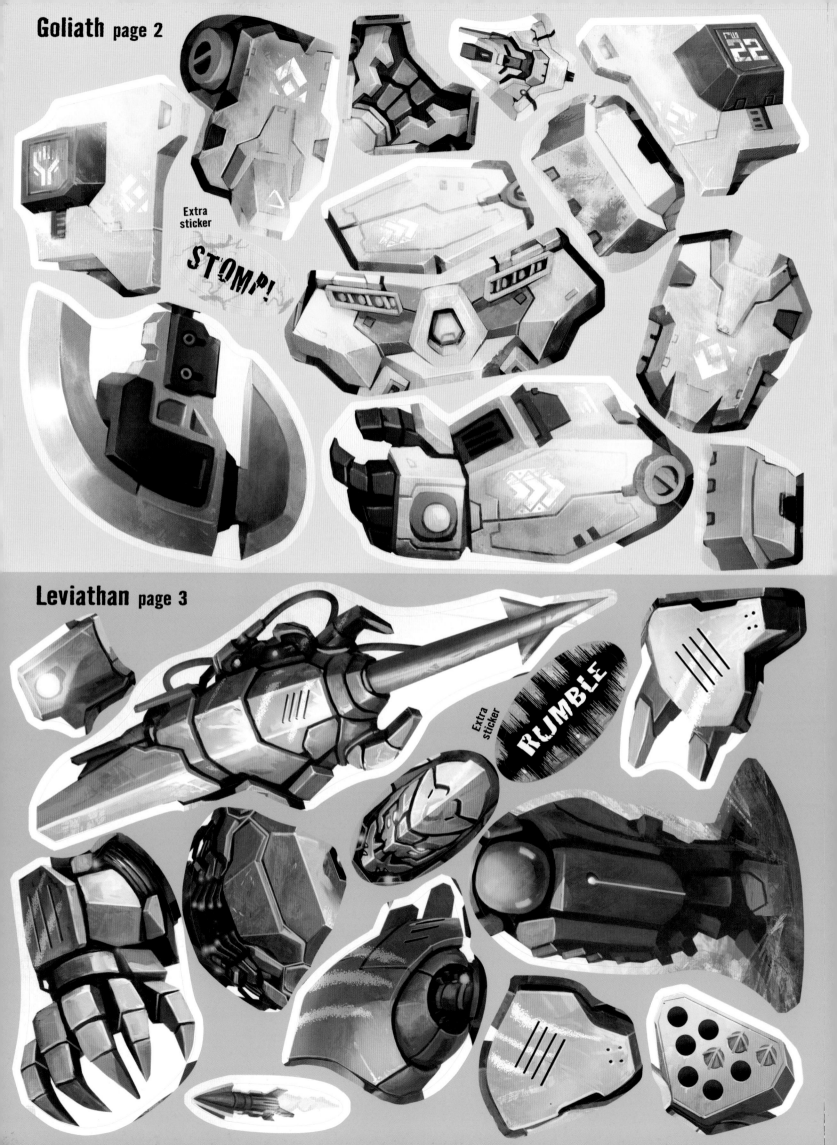

Goliath page 2

Extra sticker

STOMP!

Leviathan page 3

Extra sticker

RUMBLE

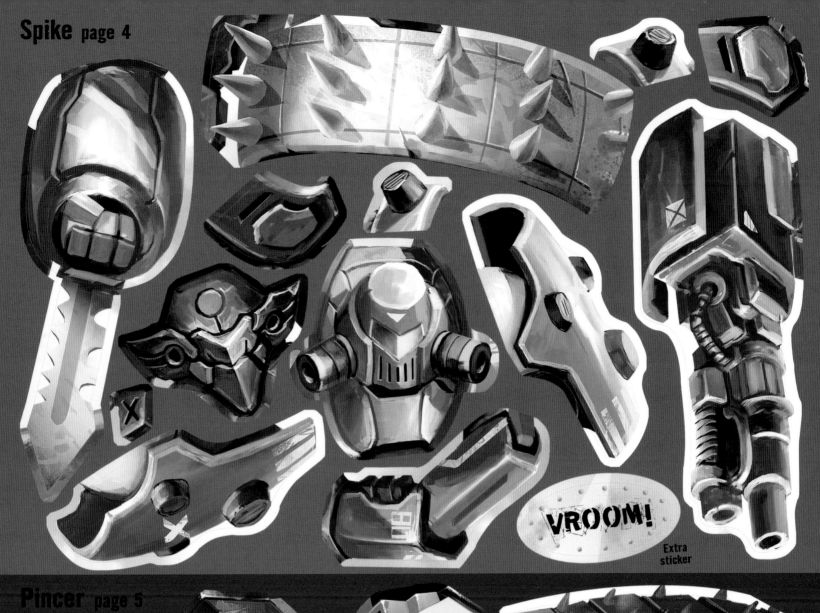

VROOM!

Extra sticker

CRUNCH

Extra sticker

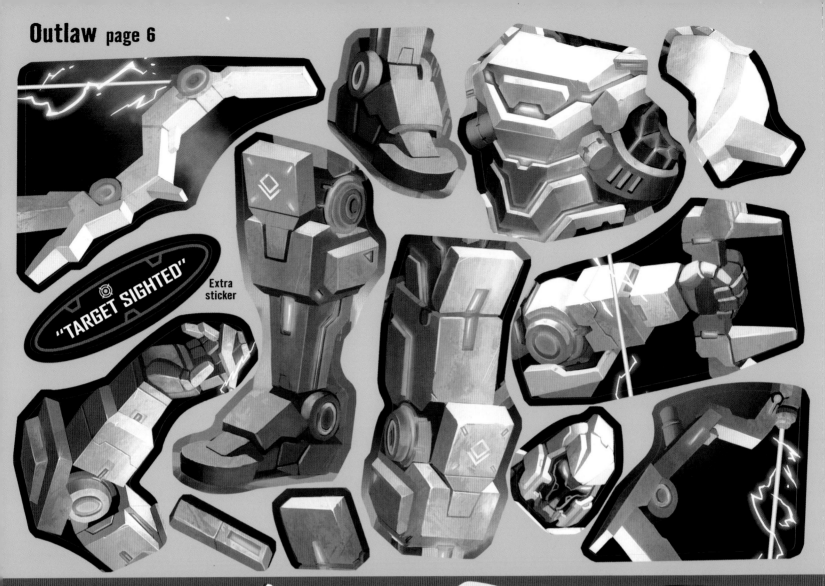

"TARGET SIGHTED"
Extra sticker

Extra sticker

SYSTEM ERROR

Extra sticker

ROAR

BLAST!

Extra
sticker

Ironstein page 11

"Ssscorax!"

Extra
sticker

Wrench page 12

Katana page 13

Kreeper page 14

Magnotron page 15

Extra sticker

"ARGHHH"

Titan page 16

Extra sticker

"ATTACK!"

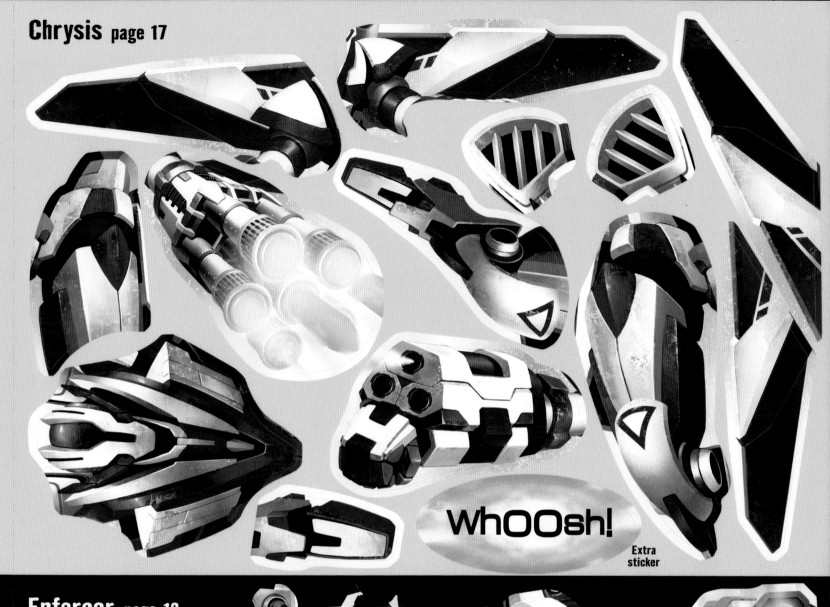

Wh00sh!

Extra
sticker

Enforcer page 18

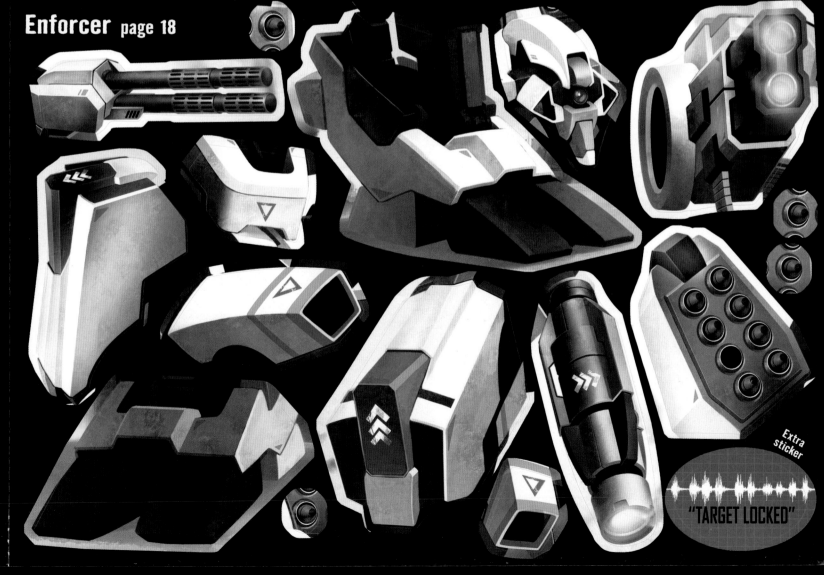

Extra
sticker

"TARGET LOCKED"

Reza page 19

Buzzsaw page 20

Nemesis page 21

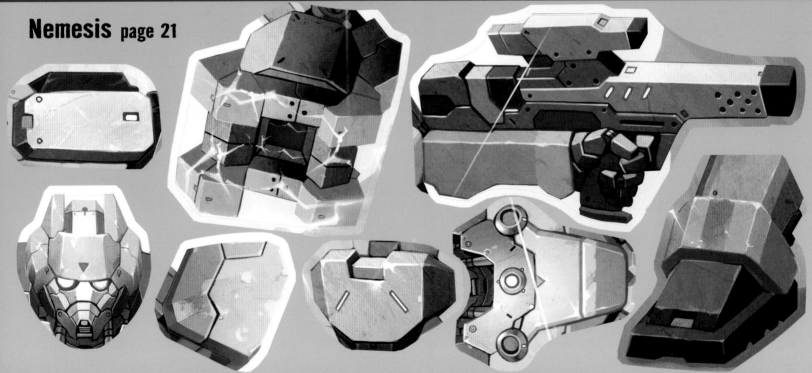

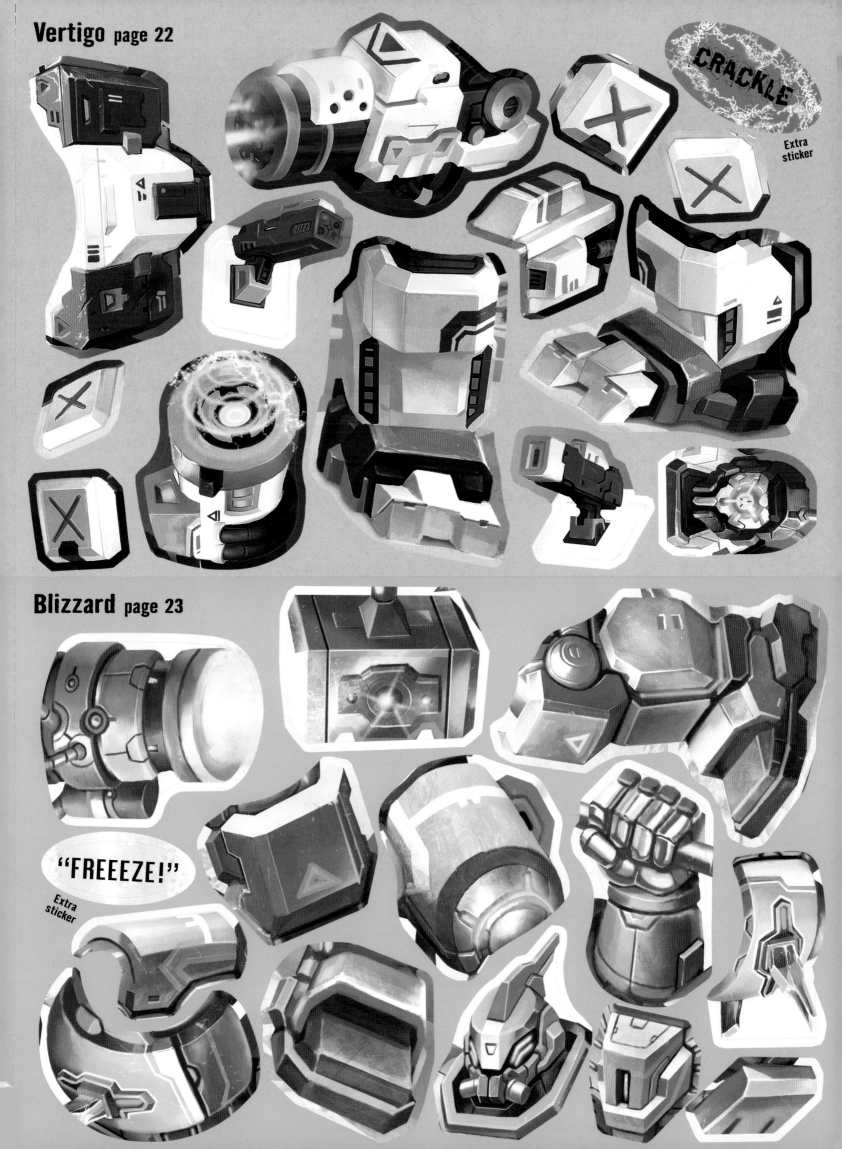

Vertigo page 22

CRACKLE

Extra sticker

Blizzard page 23

"FREEEZE!"

Extra sticker